MASSACHUSETTS BAY COLONY

TERCENTENARY

Loan Exhibition

of

One Hundred Colonial Portraits

MUSEUM OF FINE ARTS, BOSTON

19 JUNE — 21 SEPTEMBER

1930

PREFACE

For their generous provision of the present exhibition we are indebted to sixty-nine corporations and private individuals, whose names, where they have allowed it, are included in the text. We owe to the tireless labor of Mr. Frank W. Bayley the selection of the portraits exhibited and the greater part of the biographical information from which this brief catalogue is compiled; to the kindliness of the Trestle Board the fine furniture which makes the sitters appear more at their ease in the smaller gallery of the exhibition and in the adjacent gallery containing the Museum's permanent exhibition of American portraits; and to the thoughtfulness of more than one friend of the Museum the flowers which cheer the rooms.

PHILIP HENDY,
Curator, Department of Paintings.

LENDERS

Alford, Mrs. Edward B.
American Antiquarian Society
Anonymous
Bates, Mrs. Oric
Belknap, Reginald R.
Boston Athenaeum
Boston, City of
Bowditch, Mrs. Ernest W.
Bowen, John T.
Brown, Mrs. Lathrop
Campbell, Mrs. Elizabeth Knox
Cleveland Museum of Art
Codman, Russell Sturgis
Coolidge, J. Templeman
Curtis, Charles Pelham
Curtis, Mrs. Charles Pelham, Jr.
Dana, Richard Henry
Davenport, Charles M.
Davenport, George H.
DeBlois, George L.
Endicott, William Crowninshield
Fearing, Mrs. George R.
Fogg Art Museum
Foote, Rev. Henry Wilder
Gannett, Mrs. Thomas Brattle
Gardiner, William Tudor
Hamlen, Paul Mascarene
Hammond, Mrs. Gardiner Greene
Harvard Law School
Harvard University, President and Fellows of
Inches, Henderson
Joy, Mrs. Charles H.
Lockwood, Mr. and Mrs. Luke Vincent

Loring, Mrs. Atherton, Jr.
Loring, William Caleb
Marquand, Rev. Elizabeth
Massachusetts, Commonwealth of
Massachusetts Historical Society
Moseley, Mrs. Ben P. P.
Moseley, Frederick S.
Nazro, Mrs. Arthur F.
New England Historic Genealogical Society
Otis, William A.
Paine, Children of Charles J.
Pratt, Herbert Lee
Perkins, Mrs. James H.
Porter, Heirs of Mrs. Alexander S.
Rackemann, Charles S.
Rhode Island School of Design
Rhode Island, State of
Russell, Mrs. Charles F.
Saltonstall, Mrs. Richard M.
Sedgwick, Mrs. Ellery
Shattuck, Mrs. Elizabeth P.
Shattuck, Henry L.
Sleeper, Henry Davis
Spalding, Philip L.
Stevenson, Robert H.
Tilton, John Hancock
Treadwell, Grace W.
Turner, Howard M.
Updike, Daniel Berkeley
Walcott, Mrs. Robert
Warren, Estate of Winslow
Wendell, Mrs. Barrett
Wheelwright, Mrs. Edmund M.

Winslow, Mrs. George S.

ARTISTS

JOHN ADAMS, 1735–1826

Appointed by Boston to oppose the Stamp Act. Joint author of the Declaration of Independence. Peace Commissioner 1783. First Vice-President of the United States 1788. Second President 1797–1801.

Oil on canvas, 94 x 58.

John Singleton Copley, 1783

Lent by the Fogg Art Museum, Cambridge, Mass.

SAMUEL ADAMS, 1722–1803

Representative of the Massachusetts Legislature 1765–74.
Delegate to the Continental Congress 1774–81. Author of the Massachusetts "Committees of Correspondence." Signatory and largely author of the Declaration of Independence. Lieutenant Governor of Massachusetts 1789–94. Governor 1794–7.

[Oil on canvas, 50 x 40.

John Singleton Copley, 1738–1815

Lent by the City of Boston.

ISAAC ADDINGTON, 1645–1715

Speaker of the General Court of the Massachusetts Bay Colony 1685. Clerk to the Council of Safety 1689. Secretary of the Province of Massachusetts Bay 1690–1715. Chief Justice of the Superior Court of Massachusetts 1702–3. Judge of the Probate Court of Suffolk County.

Oil on canvas, 29¾ x 25½.

Anonymous

Lent by the New England Historic Genealogical Society.

SIR JEFFREY AMHERST, 1717-97

Commander in chief of the British army in North America 1758-64. Governor General of British North America 1760. Created Baron 1776. There are towns of Amherst in Massachusetts, New Hampshire and Nova Scotia.

Oil on canvas, 31½ x 26¼.

Joseph Blackburn, 1758

Lent by Herbert Lee Pratt.

SIR EDMUND ANDROS, 1637–1713

Governor of New York 1674–81. Governor of New England 1686–9. Deposed and imprisoned by the people of Boston 1689. Governor of Virginia 1692–8.

Oil on canvas, 35¾ x 29.

Anonymous

Lent by the State of Rhode Island.

MRS. CHARLES APTHORP, 1709–96

Grizell Eastwick.

Oil on canvas, 50 x 39¾.

Robert Feke, c. 1725–c. 1769

Lent by Mrs. Ben P. P. Moseley.

SUSAN APTHORP, 1734–1815

Married Thomas Bulfinch (*q.v.*) 1759.

Oil on canvas, 50 x 39¾.

Joseph Blackburn, 1757

Lent by J. Templeman Coolidge.

THEODORE ATKINSON, JR., 1733-69

Son of Colonel Theodore Atkinson. Married his cousin Frances Wentworth of Boston 1762. Secretary of the Province of New Hampshire 1762-9.

Oil on canvas, 49½ x 39¾.

Joseph Blackburn, painting 1753-63

Lent by the Rhode Island School of Design, Providence, R. I.

DR. JOSHUA BABCOCK, 1707–88

Chief Justice of the Supreme Court of Rhode Island.   An incorporator of Brown University.

Oil on canvas, 44¾ x 36½.

Joseph Blackburn, 1761

Lent by Mrs. Ernest W. Bowditch.

MRS. JOSEPH BARRELL

Hannah Fitch.

Pastel on paper, 24 x 17¾.

John Singleton Copley, 1771

Lent by Mrs. Charles H. Joy.

JOHN BARRETT, 1708–86

An active revolutionary, he redeemed in gold paper money paid to the Colonial troops in Boston. One of a committee of six which recommended the embargo upon British goods.

Oil on canvas, 49¾ x 39¾.

John Singleton Copley, 1738–1815

Lent by Mrs. Barrett Wendell.

MRS. JOHN BARRETT, 1711–98

Sarah Gerrish.

Oil on canvas, 49¾ x 39¾.

John Singleton Copley, 1738–1815

Lent by Mrs. Barrett Wendell.

JONATHAN BELCHER, 1682–1757

Boston merchant. Sent to England as agent of the Province of Massachusetts 1729. Governor of Massachusetts and New Hampshire 1730–41. Governor of New Jersey 1747–57.

Oil on canvas, 48¼ x 39½.

Thomas Hudson, 1701–79

Lent by the President and Fellows of Harvard University.

SIMON BRADSTREET, 1603–97

Secretary of the Massachusetts Bay Colony 1630–6.   Governor 1679–86, and, between the charters, 1689–92.   He had refused to serve when appointed Councillor of the Dominion of New England 1686.

Oil on canvas, 29⅞ x 25⅝.

Anonymous

Lent by the Boston Athenaeum.

WILLIAM BRATTLE, 1702–76

Preacher, lawyer and physician. Major General of militia. A loyalist and friend of General Gage, he embarked with the British troops for Halifax 1776.

Oil on canvas, 49½ x 39¾.

John Singleton Copley, 1738–1815

Lent by Mrs. Thomas Brattle Gannett.

THOMAS BULFINCH, 1728–1802

Son of Thomas Bulfinch, Boston physician, and his wife Judith Colman. Father of Charles Bulfinch, Boston architect. Studied medicine in England, returning to Boston 1757.

Oil on canvas, 30 x 26.

Joseph Blackburn, painting 1753–63

Lent by J. Templeman Coolidge.

16

THE REVEREND MATHER BYLES, 1706–88

Pastor of Hollis Street Church in Boston 1733–76.

Oil on canvas, 30¼ x 25¼.

John Singleton Copley, 1767

Lent by the American Antiquarian Society, Worcester, Mass.

CHARLES CHAMBERS, 1660–1743

Boston merchant. Selectman and Representative. Judge of the Court of Common Pleas of the Province of Massachusetts. Justice of the Peace for the County of Middlesex.

Oil on canvas, 47¾ x 37¾.

John Smibert, 1684–1751

Lent by Russell Sturgis Codman.

PETER CHARDON, JR., 1737–66

Last of the family of Chardon commemorated by Chardon Street in Boston.   Studied law.
"This fellow's thoughts are not employed on songs and girls, nor his time on flutes, fiddles, con-
certs, and card tables: he will make something" (John Adams, *Diary*, 11 October 1758).

Pastel on paper, 22½ x 17¾.

John Singleton Copley, 1738–1815

Lent by Mrs. Edmund M. Wheelwright.

JOHN CONY, 1655–1722

Boston silversmith.   Engraved the plate for the first paper money of the Massachusetts Bay
Colony.   Brother-in-law of the wife of Jeremiah Dummer (*q.v.*)   Master of Paul Revere.

Oil on canvas, 29¾ x 25.

Jeremiah Dummer, 1708

Lent by Henry Davis Sleeper.

JOHN SINGLETON COPLEY, 1738–1815

Born in Boston. Pupil perhaps of his step father Peter Pelham (*q.v.*).
Anonymous exhibitor at the Royal Academy in London 1760.
Fellow of the Society of Artists of Great Britain 1767. Left Boston for London 1774. A.R.A.
1777. R.A. 1779.

Oil on canvas, 18⅛ diameter.

Self Portrait

Lent by Mrs. Gardiner Greene Hammond.

ERRATA

5. Sir Edmund Andros: after *Anonymous* read, *copied by Batcheller, 1871.*

38. Mrs. Ezekiel Goldthwait: the reproduction and the dimensions have been erroneously interchanged with No. 58, Dorothy Murray.

58. Dorothy Murray: the reproduction and the dimensions have been erroneously interchanged with No. 38, Mrs. Ezekiel Goldthwait.

65. Henry Pelham: after *John Singleton Copley*, instead of 1752, read, *1738–1815.*

MRS. THOMAS CRANSTON

Mary Coggeshall. Daughter of Joseph Coggeshall of Newport, R. I. Married the Hon.
Thomas Cranston, grandson of Samuel Cranston, Governor of Rhode Island.

Oil on canvas, 50 x 40.

John Singleton Copley, 1738–1815

Lent by Daniel Berkeley Updike.

22

MRS. NATHANIEL CUNNINGHAM, 1732–59

Oil on canvas, 49¾ x 40.

John Greenwood, 1727–92

Lent by the heirs of Mrs. Alexander S. Porter.

23

RICHARD DANA, 1699–1772

Boston jurist.   Chairman of a committee which instructed the representatives of Boston con-
cerning the Stamp Act 1765–70.   Member of the association of Sons of Liberty.

Oil on canvas, 50 x 40.

John Singleton Copley, 1738–1815

Lent by Richard Henry Dana.

GILBERT DE BLOIS, 1725–92

Boston merchant. Held offices under the British government, remained loyal and was proscribed and banished 1778.

Oil on canvas, 36¼ x 27⅞.

John Singleton Copley, 1738–1815

Lent by George L. DeBlois.

PAUL DUDLEY, F.R.S., 1675–1752

Attorney General of the Province of Massachusetts 1702–18.   Justice of the Supreme Court
1718.   Chief Justice 1745.   Author of essays on the natural history of New England published
by the Royal Society in London 1720–35.

Oil on canvas, 30 x 25.

Anonymous

Lent by the Boston Athenaeum.

MRS. PAUL DUDLEY, 1685–1756

Lucy Wainwright.

Oil on canvas, 30 x 25.

Anonymous

Lent by the Boston Athenaeum.

JEREMIAH DUMMER, 1645–1718

Boston silversmith. Apprentice to John Hull 1659–66. Selectman of Boston. Treasurer of the County. Justice of the Peace. Appointed on the Council of Safety 1689. Printed the first paper money for Connecticut 1709–13.

Oil on canvas, 29½ x 24¾.

Self Portrait, 1691

Lent by Paul Mascarene Hamlen.

MRS. JEREMIAH DUMMER, 1652–

Anna Atwater.   Wife of Jeremiah Dummer the silversmith.

Oil on canvas, 29½ x 24¾.

Jeremiah Dummer, 1691

Lent by Paul Mascarene Hamlen.

JEREMIAH DUMMER, JR., *c.* 1679–1739

Son of Jeremiah Dummer (*q.v.*) the silversmith. Preacher and writer. Agent of Massachusetts in England 1710–21.

Oil on canvas, 50¼ x 41.

Sir Godfrey Kneller, 1646–1723

Lent by Paul Mascarene Hamlen.

WILLIAM DUMMER, 1677–1761

Son of Jeremiah Dummer (*q.v.*) the silversmith. Lieutenant Governor of the Province of Massachusetts Bay 1716–30. Acting Governor 1723–8 and 1729–30.

Oil on canvas, 51 x 40¼.

Sir Godfrey Kneller, 1646–1723

Lent by Paul Mascarene Hamlen.

JOSEPH DWIGHT, 1703–65

Brigadier General at the siege of Louisburg 1745. Judge of the Court of Common Pleas for
Hampshire County 1753–61. Judge of Probate for Berkshire County 1761–5.

Oil on canvas, 49½ x 38½.

Joseph Blackburn, painting 1753–63

Lent by Charles S. Rackemann.

JOHN ENDECOTT, *c.* 1588–1665

Governor of Massachusetts Bay Colony 1629, 1644–5, 1649–50, 1651–4, 1655–65.

Oil on canvas, 39¼ x 33¾.

Anonymous

Lent by William Crowninshield Endicott.

ROBERT FEKE, 1705-69

Settled *c.* 1726 at Newport, where he probably met John Smibert.   Married Eleanor Cozzens at Newport 1742.   Painting in Boston 1741 and 1748-9.   In Philadelphia 1746.

Oil on canvas, 29¾ x 26.

Self Portrait

Lent by the Reverend Henry Wilder Foote.

GENERAL THE HON'?Ŀ THO.Ŀ GAGE
OBᵗ 1788

THOMAS GAGE, *c.* 1720–87

Military Governor of Montreal 1760. Commander in chief of the British army in North America 1763–73. Last royal Governor of the Province of Massachusetts 1774–5, recalled after the battle of Bunker Hill.

Oil on canvas, 50 x 39¾.

John Singleton Copley, 1738–1815

Lent by Frederick S. Moseley.

MOSES GILL, 1733–1800

Lieutenant Governor of Massachusetts 1794–1800.

Oil on canvas, 49½ x 39¾.

John Singleton Copley, 1738–1815

Lent by the Rhode Island School of Design, Providence, R. I.

EZEKIEL GOLDTHWAIT, 1710–82

Town clerk of Boston.   Registrar of Deeds for the County of Suffolk.

Oil on canvas, 50 x 40.

John Singleton Copley, 1738–1815

Lent by John T. Bowen.

MRS. EZEKIEL GOLDTHWAIT, 1714-94

Elizabeth Lewis.

Oil on canvas, 36¼ x 28.

John Singleton Copley, 1738-1815

Lent by John T. Bowen.

HARRISON GRAY, 1711–94

Representative of Boston in the General Court of the Próvince of Massachusetts 1750–2.
The last royal Receiver General of the Province of Massachusetts.   Proscribed and banished
1778.

Oil on canvas, 30½ x 21½.

John Singleton Copley, 1738–1815

Lent by William A. Otis.

JOSEPH GREEN, 1706–80

Boston poet. Appointed by General Gage (*q.v.*) to the "Mandamus" Council for remodelling the government of Massachusetts 1774. Proscribed and banished 1776. Author of satyrical verse, including *The Wonderful Lament of Old Mr. Tenor* 1744, and *Poems and Satires* 1780.

Pastel on paper, 24 x 17.

John Singleton Copley, 1738–1815

Museum of Fine Arts, Boston.

40

WILLIAM GREENE, 1696–1758

Governor of Rhode Island 1743–58.

Oil on canvas, 29 x 25.

Peter Pelham, 1684–1751

Lent by Mrs. Charles Pelham Curtis, Jr.

JEREMIAH GRIDLEY, 1702–67

Editor for a year of *The Rehearsal*, founded in Boston 1731, and constant contributor.   Member of the General Court and Selectman of Brookline.   Attorney General of the Province of Massachusetts Bay 1742–67.

Oil on canvas, 27½ x 21½.

John Smibert, 1731

Lent by the Harvard Law School.

JOHN HANCOCK, 1737–93

President of the Provincial Congress 1774–5.   President of the Continental Congress 1775–7.
First signatory of the Declaration of Independence.   Governor of Massachusetts 1780–5 and
1787–93.

Oil on canvas, 49½ x 40.

John Singleton Copley, 1738–1815

Lent by the City of Boston.

MRS. JOHN HANCOCK, 1747–1829

Dorothy Quincy.

Oil on canvas, 50 x 39¾.

John Singleton Copley, 1738–1815

Lent by Mrs. Atherton Loring, Jr.

THOMAS HANCOCK, 1703–64

Foster father of John Hancock (*q.v.*). Boston merchant. Founded the Hancock Professorship of Hebrew and other Oriental languages at Harvard University.

Pastel on paper, 24 x 18½.

John Singleton Copley, 1738–1815

Lent by John Hancock Tilton.

45

MRS. THOMAS HANCOCK, 1714–77

Lydia Henchman.

Pastel on paper, 24 x 18½.

John Singleton Copley, 1738–1815

Lent by John Hancock Tilton.

EDWARD HOLYOKE, 1689–1769

President of Harvard University 1737–69.

Oil on canvas, 50¾ x 41.

John Singleton Copley, 1738–1815

Lent by the President and Fellows of Harvard University.

47

ROBERT CHAMBLETT HOOPER, 1709–90

Merchant of Marblehead.   Known in New England as "King Hooper".   His house was the headquarters of General Gage 1774.

Oil on canvas, 50 x 39¾.

John Singleton Copley, 1767

Lent by Mrs. Lathrop Brown.

ROBERT HOOPER, JR., 1746–81

Oil on canvas, 49¾ x 40¼.

John Singleton Copley, 1738–1815

Lent by Robert H. Stevenson.

NATHANIEL HURD, 1730–77

Boston engraver and silversmith.

Oil on canvas, 30¼ x 25¼.

John Singleton Copley, 1738–1815

Lent by the Cleveland Museum of Art, Cleveland, Ohio.

THOMAS HUTCHINSON, 1711–80

Representative in the General Court of the Province of Massachusetts 1737–8 and 1740–9.
Speaker 1746–8. Judge of Probate 1752. Lieutenant Governor 1758–70. Chief Justice
1760. Governor 1770–4. Author of *The History of Massachusetts Bay* 1769–7 and 1828.

Oil on canvas, 28¼ x 23½.

Edward Truman

Lent by the Massachusetts Historical Society.

MRS. HENDERSON INCHES

Sarah Jackson. Daughter of the Reverend Joseph Jackson.

Oil on canvas, 49¾ x 40.

John Singleton Copley, 1765

Lent by Mrs. Oric Bates.

JOHN LOVELL, 1710–78

Principal of the Latin School in Boston 1734–75. Delivered the first published address at Faneuil Hall in Boston 1743, on the death of Peter Faneuil, the donor. Embarked with British troops for Halifax 1776.

Oil on canvas, 30 x 26.

Nathaniel Smibert, d. c. 1757

Lent by the President and Fellows of Harvard University.

THOMAS MARSHALL, 1719–1800

Selectman of Boston 1772–6. Lieutenant Colonel of militia 1767–71. Colonel of the Tenth Massachusetts Regiment in the War of the Revolution. Fought under Washington at Valley Forge.

Oil on canvas, 49½ x 38⅜.

John Singleton Copley, 1738–1815

Lent by Mrs. Elizabeth Knox Campbell.

JEAN PAUL MASCARENE, 1684–1760

Commander in chief of the British forces in Nova Scotia. Councillor 1720. Acting Governor 1740–9. Major General 1758. Died in Boston.

Oil on canvas, 40½ x 31½.

John Smibert, 1684–1751

Lent by Paul Mascarene Hamlen.

THE REVEREND COTTON MATHER, F.R.S., 1663–1728

Ordained as colleague with his father Increase Mather as Minister of the North Church in Boston 1685.   Advocate of innoculation for small pox.   Author of 382 works, including *Essays to do Good* 1710.

Oil on canvas, 30¼ x 25¼.

Peter Pelham, 1727

Lent by the American Antiquarian Society, Worcester, Mass.

RICHARD MIDDLECOTT, 1633 (?)–1704

Came to New England c. 1670.   Married Sarah, daughter of John Winslow.

Oil on canvas, 29¾ x 26.

N. Byfield, 1713

Lent by Mrs. Richard M. Saltonstall.

DOROTHY MURRAY, 1743–1811

Born in Scotland. Married John Forbes in Boston 1769. Lived in Florida 1769–73. In Boston 1773–1811.

Oil on canvas, 50 x 39¾.

John Singleton Copley, 1738–1815

Lent by the Fogg Art Museum, Cambridge, Mass.

DANIEL, ANDREW, and PETER OLIVER

Daniel, 1704–27. Andrew, 1706–74, became Secretary and Lieutenant Governor of the Province of Massachusetts Bay. Peter, 1713–91, became Chief Justice. Sons of Daniel Oliver, 1663–1732, of Cambridge, Mass.

Oil on canvas, 39¾ x 57½.   *John Smibert, 1684–1751*

Lent Anonymously.

JAMES OTIS, 1702–78

Member of the General Court of the Province of Massachusetts 1758.   Speaker 1760–2.
Judge of Probate 1763.   Chief Justice of the Court of Common Pleas 1764.   Member of the
Council for the Province of Massachusetts 1770.

Oil on canvas, 49¾ x 40¼.

John Singleton Copley, 1738–1815

Lent by William A. Otis.

MRS. JAMES OTIS, b. 1702

Mary Allyne.   Daughter of Joseph Allyne of Plymouth, Mass. The mother of thirteen children, she died before 1755, when James Otis (*q.v.*) married again.

Oil on canvas, 50 x 39¾.

John Singleton Copley, 1738–1815

Lent by William A. Otis.

JAMES OTIS, JR., 1725–83

Son of James Otis (*q.v.*).   Lawyer at Plymouth from 1748.   Spoke in the State House in Boston against the writs of assistance 1761.   Author of *The Rights of the Colonies Vindicated* 1764.

Oil on canvas, 29½ x 25¼.

Joseph Blackburn, 1755

Lent by Mrs. Charles F. Russell.

MRS. JAMES OTIS, JR., 1728–89

Ruth Cunningham.   Daughter of Nathaniel and Ann Boucher Cunningham.
Oil on canvas, 29½ x 25¼.

Joseph Blackburn, 1755

Lent by Mrs. Charles F. Russell.

ROBERT TREAT PAINE, 1731–1814

Conducted the prosecution of Captain Preston for firing on inhabitants of Boston 1770. Delegate to the Continental Congress 1774–8. Signatory of the Declaration of Independence. Attorney General of Massachusetts 1779–90. Judge of the Supreme Court 1790–1804.

Oil on canvas, 29½ x 24¼.

Edward Savage, 1761–1817

Lent by the children of the late General Charles J. Paine.

HENRY PELHAM, 1749–1806

Son of Peter Pelham (*q.v.*) and Mary Singleton Copley, and thus half brother to John Singleton Copley (*q.v.*).

Oil on canvas, 30¼ x 25.

John Singleton Copley, 1752

Lent anonymously.

PETER PELHAM, 1684 (?)–1751

Painter and mezzotint engraver.   Came to Boston from London 1726.
Married Mary Singleton Copley, mother of John Singleton Copley (*q.v.*).

Oil on canvas, 34¾ x 27¾.

John Singleton Copley, 1738–1815

Lent by Charles Pelham Curtis.

MARY PEMBERTON, b. 1717

Born probably in Boston.   Sister of Samuel Pemberton (*q.v.*).

Oil on canvas, 30¼ x 25¼.

John Smibert, 1684–1751

Lent by George H. Davenport.

SAMUEL PEMBERTON, 1723–79

Born probably in Boston.   Brother of Mary Pemberton (*q.v.*).

Oil on canvas, 30¼ x 25½.

John Smibert, 1684–1751

Lent by George H. Davenport.

WILLIAM PEPPERELL, 1646–1734

Boston merchant. Justice of the Peace 1690–1725. Judge of the Court of Common Pleas of the Province of Massachusetts 1694–1702 and 1708–20. Lieutenant Colonel of Militia.

Oil on canvas, 30 x 23.

John Smibert, 1684–1751

Lent by Reginald R. Belknap.

SPENCER PHIPS, 1685–1757

Spencer Bennett took by statute the surname of his uncle Sir William Phips (*q.v.*).   Lieutenant Governor of the Province of Massachusetts Bay 1732–57.   Acting Governor 1749–53 and 1756–7.

Oil on canvas, 30 x 25.

John Smibert, 1684–1751

Lent by Henry L. Shattuck.

SIR WILLIAM PHIPS, 1650–95

Sheriff of New England 1688. Commander of the naval forces against the French in Canada 1690. Captain General and Governor in chief of the Province of Massachusetts 1692–5. Summoned to England to answer complaints 1694.

Oil on canvas, 30¼ x 25.

Thomas Child, d. 1706

Lent by William Tudor Gardiner.

MRS. JOHN POWELL, 1684–1764

Anna Dummer.   Daughter of Jeremiah Dummer (*q.v.*) the silversmith.

Oil on canvas, 49½ x 39½.

John Singleton Copley, 1764

Lent by Mrs. Ellery Sedgwick.

SAMUEL QUINCY, 1735–89

Solicitor General for the Province of Massachusetts Bay.   A loyalist, he left New England
1776.   Attorney General of Antigua 1776–89.

Oil on canvas, 35½ x 27½.

John Singleton Copley, 1738–1815

Lent by Grace W. Treadwell.

73

EDWARD RAWSON, 1615–93

Secretary of Massachusetts Bay Colony 1650–86.   Recorder of the County of Suffolk 1651–70.

Oil on canvas, 42 x 34.

Anonymous, 1670

Lent by the New England Historic Genealogical Society.

REBECCA RAWSON, 1656–92

Daughter of Edward and Rachel Perne Rawson.

Oil on canvas, 39½ x 33¼.

Anonymous, 1670

Lent by the New England Historic Genealogical Society.

THE ROYALL FAMILY

Penelope Royall, sister to Isaac Royall, Jr., Mrs. Mary Palmer, sister to Mrs. Isaac Royall, Jr. Mrs. Isaac Royall, Jr., and her daughter Elizabeth Royall. Isaac Royall, Jr., 1719-81, founded the Royall Professorship of Law in Harvard College.

Oil on canvas, 56 x 78.

Robert Feke, 1741

Lent by the Harvard Law School.

CHAMBERS RUSSELL, 1713-67

Justice of the Superior Court of Massachusetts 1752–66.

Oil on canvas, 29¼ x 24¾.

Edward Truman

Lent by Mrs. George R. Fearing.

MRS. CHAMBERS RUSSELL, 1716–62

Mary Wainwright.

Oil on canvas, 49¾ x 40.

Joseph Blackburn, painting 1753–63

Lent by the Reverend Elizabeth Marquand.

78

SIR RICHARD SALTONSTALL, 1586–1658 (?)

Member and assistant of the Massachusetts Bay Company 1629. Landed from the "Arbella", organized the settlement at Watertown 1630–1 and returned to England. Patentee of Connecticut 1635. British Ambassador to Holland 1644.

Oil on panel, 32¾ x 23.

Dutch, Anonymous

Lent by Mrs. Richard M. Saltonstall.

RICHARD SALTONSTALL, 1703–56

Representative of Haverhill in the General Court of the Massachusetts Bay Colony 1728.
Judge of the Superior Court of Massachusetts 1736–56.

Oil on canvas, 49¾ x 39¾.

Robert Feke, c. 1725–c. 1769

Lent by Mrs. Richard M. Saltonstall.

THOMAS SAVAGE, 1608–82

Came to Massachusetts with Sir Henry Vane (*q.v.*) 1635. Freeman of Boston 1636. Later Town Clerk and Selectman. Representative in the General Court of the Massachusetts Bay Colony 1654. A founder of the settlement of Rhode Island 1638.

Oil on canvas, 65 x 37.

Anonymous, 1679

Lent by Mrs. Elizabeth P. Shattuck.

JOHN SCOLLAY, 1712–90

Selectman of Boston 1754–64 and 1773–4.   Chairman of the Board of Selectmen 1774–90.
Oil on canvas, 36 x 29½.

John Singleton Copley, 1738–1815

Lent by Mrs. James H. Perkins.

WILLIAM SHIRLEY, 1693–1771

Governor of the Province of Massachusetts Bay 1741–56. Planned the expedition against Cape Breton, treated with the Eastern Indians and explored the Kennebec. Commander in chief of the British army in North America 1755. Lieutenant General 1759.

Oil on canvas, 49⅛ x 39¾.

Thomas Hudson, 1701–79

Lent by the Commonwealth of Massachusetts.

83

SAMUEL SHUTE, 1653–1742

Governor of the Province of Massachusetts Bay 1716–23.

Oil on canvas, 30 x 25¼.

Peter Pelham, 1684–1751

Lent by Mrs. Thomas Brattle Gannett.

JOHN SPOONER, b. 1728

Boston merchant.

Oil on canvas, 30 x 25¾.

John Singleton Copley, 1738–1815

Lent by Philip L. Spalding.

85

WILLIAM STOUGHTON, 1631–1701

Lieutenant Governor of the Province of Massachusetts Bay 1692–1701. Acting Governor 1694–9 and 1700–1. First Chief Justice of Massachusetts 1692–1701.

Oil on canvas, 24¾ x 21¼.

Evert Duyckinck, 1685

Lent by the Boston Athenaeum.

WILLIAM TAILER, 1676–1732

Colonel at the taking of Port Royal 1710. Lieutenant Governor of the Province of Massachusetts Bay 1711–6 and 1730–2. Acting Governor 1715–6.

Oil on canvas, 49¾ x 40½.

John Smibert, 1684–1751

Lent by Mr. and Mrs. Luke Vincent Lockwood.

MRS. PATRICK TRACY, 1724–56

Hannah Gookin.

Oil on canvas, 35½ x 28¼.

John Greenwood, 1727–92

Lent by Mrs. Elizabeth P. Shattuck.

MRS. WILLIAM TURNER, 1746 (?) –1824

Ann Dumaresq.

Pastel on paper, 23¼ x 17½.

John Singleton Copley, 1738–1815

Lent by Howard M. Turner.

SIR HENRY VANE, 1612–62

Son of Sir Henry Vane, the Treasurer of the Royal Household to Kings James I and Charles I.
Governor of Massachusetts Bay Colony 1636–7.   Knighted 1640.   Executed in London for
his opposition to the Crown 1662.

Oil on canvas, 30 x 25¼.

Sir Peter Lely, 1618–80

Lent by Charles M. Davenport.

90

MRS. WILLIAM WALTER, 1741–98

Lydia Lynde. Daughter of Benjamin Lynde of Salem. William Walter was Rector of Trinity Church in Boston 1767–75, and of Christ Church 1792–1800.

Oil on canvas, 30 x 25½.

John Singleton Copley, 1738–1815

Lent by Mrs. Robert Walcott.

JAMES WARREN, 1726–1808

President of the Provincial Congress of Massachusetts 1774.

Oil on canvas, 51¼ x 41.

John Singleton Copley, 1738–1815

Lent by the estate of Winslow Warren.

MRS. JAMES WARREN, 1728–1815

Mercy Otis.   Daughter of James Otis (*q.v.*).

Cil on canvas, 51¼ x 41.

John Singleton Copley, 1738–1815

Lent by the estate of Winslow Warren.

GEORGE WATSON, 1718–1800

Plymouth merchant. At one time owner of Clark's Island in Plymouth Harbor, where the Pilgrims made a temporary landing.

Oil on canvas, 50 x 40⅛.

John Singleton Copley, 1765

Lent by Henderson Inches.

MRS. GEORGE WATSON, 1735–67

Elizabeth Oliver. Daughter of Chief Justice Peter Oliver (*see* Daniel, Andrew and Peter Oliver). George Watson's second wife.

Oil on canvas, 50 x 40.

John Singleton Copley, 1738–1815

Lent by Henderson Inches.

95

DOROTHY WENDELL

Married Richard Skinner.

Oil on canvas, 29¾ x 24¾.

Nathaniel Smibert, 1755

Lent by Mrs. Edward B. Alford.

RICHARD WIBIRD, 1702–65

Member of the Council of the Province of New Hampshire.   Judge of Probate.

Oil on canvas, 35½ x 28¼.

Joseph Badger, 1708–65

Lent by Mrs. Arthur F. Nazro.

MRS. JOSHUA WINSLOW

Hannah Loring.

Oil on canvas, 49¾ x 39.

John Singleton Copley, 1763

Lent by William Caleb Loring.

THE WINSLOW FAMILY

Isaac Winslow, 1709–77. His wife Lucy Waldo, 1724–68. Their children Lucy, 1749–70, and Hannah, 1755–c. 1819.

Oil on canvas, 58¼ x 79¾.   *Joseph Blackburn, 1757*

Lent by Mrs. George S. Winslow.

JOHN WINTHROP, 1588–1649
Governor of Massachusetts Bay Colony 1629–34, 1637–40, 1642–4 and 1646–9.
Oil on canvas, 34¾ x 28¾.
Anonymous
Lent by the American Antiquarian Society, Worcester, Mass.